A TAIL OF TWO COOPERS

A Book About Eye Drops

written by Sara Devlin

illustrated by Brandi Rebbe

A Tail of Two Coopers
A Book About Eye Drops

Written by Sara Devlin

Illustrated by Brandi Rebbe

Edited by Griffin Mill

Cover and Interior Layout by Michael Nicloy

ISBN: 978-1945907807

Published by Nico 11 Publishing & Design
Mukwonago, Wisconsin

Be well read.

Quantity orders can be emailed to:

mike@nico11publishing.com

or call 217-779-9677

Printed in the United States of America

Proceeds from sales of this book will be donated to
Pawsitive Restorations Animal Rescue and DDFL in Colorado.

Foreword

It is my honor to write the foreword for this sweet and informative book. I have been Cooper's ophthalmologist for the past few years. Cooper has amblyopia in his left eye. Amblyopia means that his brain developed a preference for his right eye due to the left eye being out of focus, making it harder for his brain to use it. An eye with amblyopia is often referred to as a "lazy eye."

Amblyopia can develop for many reasons. In Cooper's case, it developed because he was born with a cataract in the left eye. He had surgery as an infant to remove the cataract, but that was only the beginning of the visual rehabilitation needed to achieve his best possible vision in his left eye. In order to improve the vision in an amblyopic eye, the stronger eye must be penalized in order to force the brain to use the weaker eye. The most common form of penalization is wearing an eye patch over the stronger eye for anywhere from two to six hours per day. This is a challenge for a small child, and sometimes the treatment can last for years!

Thanks to some excellent nationwide studies performed by the Pediatric Eye Disease Investigator Group (PEDIG), we know that atropine penalization works just as well as patching in most cases for the treatment of amblyopia. Atropine treatment involves placing one drop of atropine 1% eye drops in the stronger eye at bedtime. This causes the stronger eye to remain blurry throughout the following day, especially at close range. The patient then uses the weaker eye preferentially, which strengthens the vision. For many kids, who become frustrated and exhausted of wearing their eye patch for multiple hours per day over months or even years, having the option to choose atropine treatment can be a game changer! Cooper has been successfully using atropine eye drops to treat his amblyopia for over a year. Like most patients, he has tolerated the treatment well without significant side effects. To my knowledge, this is the first book describing a patient's experience with atropine treatment for amblyopia. I applaud Cooper and his mother for writing it, and I hope it will provide education and comfort to other families facing the same treatment.

Anna Steele, MD
Pediatric Ophthalmologist
Children's Eye Physicians, Denver, Colorado

Thank you to all the wonderful eye doctors who dedicate their lives, so we may see the beauty of the world. Also, thank you to all the animal rescue workers. You made sure my two furry loves made it safely to me and my family to be loved furever.

-Sara

Hi! This is Cooper. He is five.

When he was a little baby, a doctor
discovered he had a cataract in his eye.
That's basically like having a cloud over your eye.
It makes it hard to see.

Doctors removed the cloud and now
Cooper wears special glasses.

Cooper use to patch every day for many hours.
He wore an eye patch over his "strong" eye so that
his "weak" eye could get a workout.

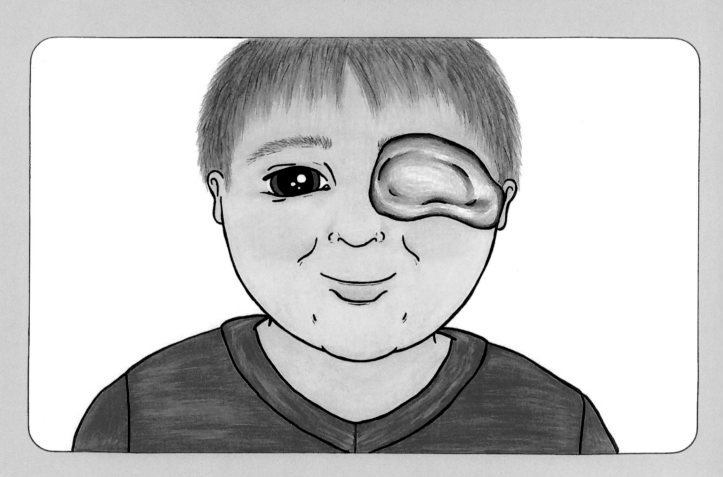

When he entered full-day Kindergarten,
the patching was too much for him.

He needed to try something else.

His doctor suggested he try eye drops.

At night, right before bed, Cooper's parents
put one eye drop into his "strong" eye.

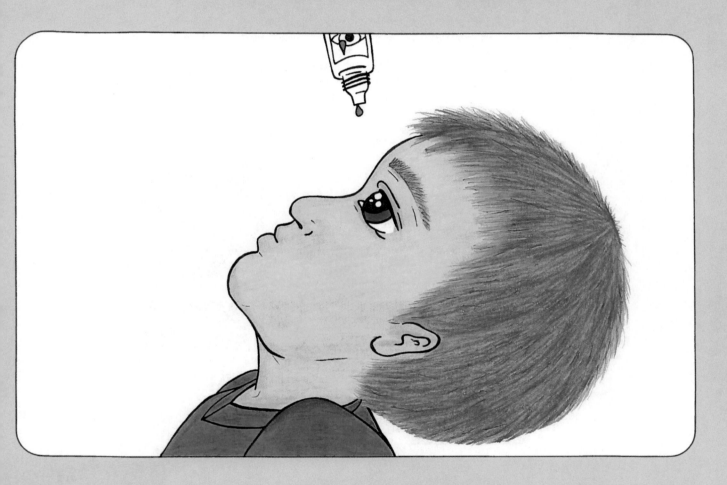

The drop makes his "strong" eye a little blurry so that his
"weak" eye can still get a workout when Cooper is at school
and throughout his day. Putting the drop in his eye is not
always fun, but Cooper knows that it helps him see!

One day Cooper's family decided to add a new member to their family.

They went down to the local animal shelter
and found a perfect dog for them.

The dog came into a small "meet and greet" room at the shelter with Cooper, Tyler, Will, and their Mom and Dad and somehow managed to not knock over anyone with his huge, strong tail.

He had eyes that twinkled and a big doggie grin.
He loved to be petted and get treats.
He was the perfect addition to the big, busy, family full of boys.

There was only one funny thing about the new dog.
His name was also Cooper!

So, when Cooper's mom called Cooper the boy over to brush his teeth, Cooper the dog would come over ready to get his teeth brushed too.

When Cooper's Mom asked Cooper the boy to put his clothes on for school, Cooper the dog was ready to put on a pair of pants.

When Cooper the boy was naughty and got put into timeout,
Cooper the dog thought he needed to go to time out too.

Nighttime rolled around and it was time to put in
Cooper the boy's eye drop. Who showed up to help?
Cooper the dog!

So, Mom put one drop into Cooper's "strong" eye and a pretend drop into Cooper the dog's eye. One got a hug for being such a good boy with his drops, and the other got lots of pets on the head.

Cooper the boy was so happy to have a friend to help him with his eye drops.

The end.

Sara Devlin is the mom of three wonderful and crazy boys.
She is married to her high school sweetheart.
She loves dogs, yoga, and reading books.
Cheers to high school dreams coming true.

Photo credit: Stacey Jackson

Brandi Rebbe
First, I would like to thank my husband for helping me find the time to work on this book and encouraging me to stay creative with my art. To my son and daughter Thank You BOTH for the excitement you always share with me as you watch me take an idea and bring it to life on paper.

Photo credit: Jenelle Collins

A BIG Thanks to my friends and family who continue to cheer me on through every book I illustrate. I'm very excited I was able to collaborate with my childhood friend, Sara, and create our third book!!! I hope everyone enjoys the adorable Tale of Two Coopers!!

Other books by Sara Devlin!

Cooper's Mighty Eye
A Story About Patching

It's YOUR Chance
to be a
SUPERHERO!

Made in the USA
Monee, IL
16 April 2021